"The Lord is my strength and song."
Exodus 15:2

God made you

SPECIAL!

In the space below, can you draw something that is special to you?

Date _____

"For by Him all things were created."
Colossians 1:16

"Every good gift and every perfect gift is from above."
James 1:17

"I will sing and make music with all my soul."
Psalm 108:1

"For He Himself is our peace."
Ephesians 2:14

"The Lord is good to all."
Psalm 145:9

"God shall supply all your needs."
Philippians 4:19

"A generous man will himself be blessed."
Proverbs 22:9

"One man gives freely, yet gains even more."
Proverbs 11:24

"Do good to all."
Galatians 6:10

"He makes his sun rise."
Matthew 5:45

 "A cheerful heart is good medicine."
Proverbs 17:22

"The Lord is my rock."
2 Samuel 22:2

"Trust in the Lord with all of your heart."
Proverbs 3:5

"Behold the beauty of the Lord."
Psalm 27:4

Can you color the instrument that is like the one that the angel is playing?

"Make music to him with the tambourine and harp."
Psalm 149:3

Can you connect the dots 1-10, and draw what he drew?

5 4

7 6 3

8 2

9 10 1

"Love never fails."
1 Corinthians 13:8

 **L** is for Love.

Can you circle the animals that start with the letter "L" and are showing Love?

"A friend loveth at all times."
Proverbs 17:17

K is for Kindness

Color and cut out the "Kindness Coupons."
In the circle on each coupon, draw a picture of
the person you want to share it with. Cut
these out
and show
someone
special some
kindness.

Kindness Coupon
This coupon is good for one
extra special
day together.

Kindness Coupon
This coupon is good for
whatever I can
do to make you
happy.

"Be kind to one another."
Ephesians 4:32

How many hearts do you see?
Can you circle the number?

3   1

5   4

6   2

"Love is kind."
1 Corinthians 13:4

Can you follow the garden path to help the angel find her flowers?

"I am the true vine; my Father is the gardener."
John 15:1

"You have put gladness in my heart."
Psalm 4:7

Can you trace over the ----- lines to see what is growing out of the pots?

"The seed is God's teaching."
Luke 8:11

Can you count the number of stars in the sky? Circle the number.

2   4

1   3   5

"He determines the number of stars."
Psalm 147:4

Baby starts with the letter
"B"

Do you know what letter your name
starts with?

Can you write it on the line?

_____

"A good name is more desirable than great riches."
Proverbs 22:1

Children fold their hands to pray.
Can you trace your hand in the box?

My Hand

Date_____

"Come and pray to me and I will listen to you."
Jeremiah 29:12

There are 6 (six)  in this picture.
Can you circle them all?

"Rest in the Lord."
Psalm 37:7

Can you circle the animals around the ark that are in groups of 2 (two)?

"And they went into the ark to Noah, two by two."
Genesis 7:15

"A friend sticks closer than a brother."
Proverbs 18:24

"Come my children, listen to me."
Psalm 34:11

"for by grace you have been saved."
Ephesians 2:8

Can you help this lost frog find his way back to the ark?

"Do not be afraid."
John 14:27